# Paleo Diet

# 20 Modern Paleo Diet Recipes-To Lose Weight for Beginners

# Table of Contents

# Chapter 1:

# Introduction to Paleo Diet and Ketogenic Diet

Fig 1.0

Have you ever thought about the last time when you ate something entirely healthy? Any food having no extra fat, no extra sugar, and no preservatives at all? Or the last time when you compromised on the taste but gave more preference to your health? I bet, you cannot. Because we, the humans of this generations, have become just like machines or some kind of robots who work all the time and eat whatever is available.

Gone are the good old days when people actually hunted their own food because they always looked for more and more healthy nutrients to stay healthy and active. Those were the people who preferred health over taste. Even when we have time to choose what we have to eat we always go for food that are already preserved and least healthy. Burgers, Pizza, soft drinks, fried chicken and other such foods have become our favorite to eat these days because we only have to pay and are free from the hassle of cooking for ourselves and our families. I am not sorry to tell you that these foods are not healthy at all - because the definition of healthy food is to consume rich quantity of proteins, natural fats and to avoid massive intake of calories or extra carbs.

Gone is the time when people ate and stayed healthy all the time. The chicken, meat, or grains that we intake are no more healthy because they are not fresh anymore. They are preserved. Pure healthy diet used to be the part of daily diet of human beings about millions of years ago. It consisted of ingredients which were 100% pure and were natural in true means.

  The diet consisting of 100% natural ingredients (which is hardly the parts of our diet these days) is called Paleo diet and it is nothing but the consumption of fresh and natural fruits, vegetables, meat and nuts. The main purpose of this diet is to provide you more and more amount of energy so your body stays healthy. No doubt we use all these in our diet but the problem is that these are not only the things that our diet these days contain. We consume a lot of extra calories because of huge intake of coffee, cold drink. Moreover, tea and other stuff, junk food has become an inseparable part of our lives because of which we have to intake extra fats and sugar so our diet is no more paleo. Weight gain is one of the problems that every 3$^{rd}$ individual these days faces and the main reason behind it is the intake of unhealthy diet.

The main reason behind talking about Paleo diet is to recalling the ancients ways of healthy eating because when people ate healthy they faced less problems like blood pressure, diabetes, depression and obesity. So the main idea is to consume food which is a great source of energy. The foods that you buy from shops and restaurants are never Paleo since they are packed and they have stored sugar, salts and other ingredients with them, when it comes to paleo diet, it consists of foods that we get naturally. For example, ancient people can be recalled as using Paleo diets since they never bought food or went to restaurants to get ready made food. Rather, they cultivated vegetables and fruits and hunted animals themselves. So they go all the carbs, proteins and fats naturally and that is the reason that the rats of diseases and all the issues related to health were lesser in those times as compared to today.

The diet that people usually use to lose weight and to burn extra fat and calories is called Ketogenic diet, which means to eat nothing but to stay healthy at the same time. This kind of diet includes some special items which are free from extra (harmful) fats and carbs and which are a rich source of energy as well. Not only this, such foods have the ability to burn extra fat inside the body by producing ketones so the body keeps on relying on these ketones (which is not very easy!).

The ketones replace the glucose and provide fuel to brain and liver to keep on functioning properly even when the person is not consuming usual meals. Such ketones are produced inside the bodies when a person intakes very low amount of carbohydrates and proteins and relies on very few things to eat like fish and olive oil. But this technique to lose weight is not an easy task to perform and is suggested by doctors to the patients with severe health issues like obesity and epilepsy, heartburn and acne. One of its advantages also includes increased mental focus because our brain becomes very active because of the fuel that it keeps on getting through ketones.

Like Paleo diet, ketogenic diet does not allow you to eat everything that is rich in energy (proteins and fats), rather, it only allows you to intake those foods which can keep your body insulin level very low and ketone level very high so the body would keep on burning fats. For example, Paleo diet sees potatoes and sweet potatoes as something very healthy but ketogenic diet does not.

# Chapter 2
# 5 Paleo Smoothie Recipes

When it comes to losing weight, many people start dieting and think that this is the best way to burn calories. But unfortunately, it is not so! You keep yourself starving for months and lose your health that's all what dieting is about. Moreover, it results in a number of health problems too. There is another option which is far better than dieting and it's the intake of paleo diet. This diet allows you to east anytime and every time and never tells you to compromise on your food life.

No doubt paleo diet used to be a part of what people of ancient times ate millions of years ago but it's not very much impossible to make it the part of our diet again. We will only need to put a little hard work and will have to remove junk foods and all the oily and spicy items from our diet. The replacements like juices and smoothies made up of fresh vegetables and fruits are a perfect option to keep you stay healthy without letting you compromise on the taste.

If you want to make Paleo diet a part of your routine then do not worry at all! If you cannot eat huge amounts of natural fruits, vegetables and cannot compromise on taste then the best option is to make smoothies the main part of your lives. Smoothies are always healthy because you use fresh fruits and they are a good source of natural fats, carbs, proteins, and minerals. Moreover, you can intake a huge amount of healthy fruits and green vegetables by making drinks out of them so it is one of the easiest and simplest ways to consume paleo foods. You can use these kind of smoothies a part of your daily diet by taking them with your breakfast, lunch, dinner or simple as an evening or afternoon snack. Not only they are very much healthy, but are super delicious as well!

Here is a list of top 5 Paleo smoothies which can prove to be the best for not only your health but will give a lovely feeling to your taste buds as well.

# Sun Flower chocolate Smoothie

Fig. 2.0

If you are craving for butter but you cannot have one because of health issues, try this smoothie. It can be used as the best substitute for butter spreads and you will not have to compromise on taste as well. It has sunflower seed butter in it which is the best source of zinc, iron, magnesium, fiber and vitamin E. so this butter is very good for your body and helps in quick digestion as well so you will not have to worry about weight gain. The best thing about this smoothie is that you can make it within minutes. All you need to have is some bananas, cocoa powder, almond milk and some sunflower seed butter. Mix all the ingredients, blend them and your drink is ready.

The drink is very light having only 13 grams of carbs and 17 grams of fat. The total calorie count of the drink is 369.5. Not only this, you also intake 6.25 grams of proteins through this drink as well.

# Pumpkin pie Smoothie

Fig. 2.1

This is another amazing options for you if you want to eat natural and healthy Paleo food. It can satisfy your sweet cravings and you will not have to compromise on taste. You need to mix bananas and pumpkins with some maple syrup and vanilla extract and the drink will be ready. The special thing about this smoothie is that we do not any extra sugars or sweetening ingredients in it which can prove to be bad for your health. We make it sweet by adding natural and fresh fruits and some maple syrup.   The drink has got 146 total calories in it with 50 grams of carbs (which comes from fruits only) and only 2 grams of fat so you can have it all the time without worrying about weight gain or anything. Not only this, it gives you about 3 grams of proteins as well.

# Acai boost Smoothie

Fig. 2.2

This delicious drink is made with fresh acal barriers which are really tasty and gives an alluring taste to the drink when mixed with some bananas and coconut juice. Acal barriers are very in the sense that they remove all the unhealthy (cancer and other diseases causing) toxicants from your body and keep is safe from getting viruses. They are very good for skin as well. Their intake can prove to be very useful for your body but since it is not possible to eat a huge amount of barriers at a time so it's good to make a smoothie out of them and drink it whenever you feel like. The total count of calories in the drink is only 137 grams with 7 grams of fats and 32 grams of crabs. It is a good source of proteins as well.

# Never beet Smoothie

Fig. 2.3

Beets are a very good option for you if you are looking for something healthy to intake. They are low calorie foods with only 146 grams of calories with a huge amount of fiber, vitamins, antioxidants and minerals. So, what can be healthier than this? This fruit has the ability to keep your body away from heart and blood diseases. Again when you need to intake a huge amount of beets, the best way is to make a smoothie by mixing them with some other healthy ingredients like banana, vanilla extract and coconut milk and turning them into a healthy drink. The drink has 32 grams of carbs with only 7 grams of fats. The protein intake will be 3 grams when you use this drink in your diet.

# **Green Fruit Smoothie**

Fig. 2.4

Green fruits and vegetables have all the healthy things that your body needs. Natural green fruits are a perfect example of Paleo diet and they have been proving to be the best source of energy with dozens of advantages and not a single harm or disadvantage since millions of years. You can make a smoothie out of green fruits by mixing fruits like green apples, grapes, spinach and adding some coconut water, coconut milk and raw honey for making and sweet and healthier.

You can also add bananas because they are also a very great source of energy and can be added in all kinds of smoothies to intake something healthy. The smoothie made out of green fruits has the fat count that is not more than 2 grams which is equal to having no fats at all so it is the best for you if you are scared of gaining weight. The carbs count is 55 grams but all the carb are because of fresh fruits and not because of preserved sugars which are not beneficial for health. You also intake about 3 grams of proteins when you have this drink.

# Chapter 3

# 5 Protein Rich Paleo Recipes to Build Muscles

Foods having rich amount of proteins in them are a very important part of paleo diet family because proteins are very crucial for healthy growth of body parts, especially for the muscles. They help the muscle tissues to grow properly and healthy. When you intake something that has a good amount of proteins in it, the digestive system of your body breaks the proteins into amino acids which act primarily as a vehicle to provide growth to the muscles of your body so you stay healthy and active. That is the reason behind proteins having so much importance in the Paleo diet.

Ancient people used to have a healthy Paleo diet because whatever they ate was natural and fresh and was richly supplied with proteins. They hunted animals and got their proteins from their flesh and from their milk. You can also get great amount of proteins from eggs, soy, and cold water fish.

If you want to eat Paleo diet because you want to stay healthy but you are not ready to compromise on taste then do not worry at all! We have some protein rich Paleo recipes for you which are rich in proteins, natural carbohydrates and fats and are free from extra sugar. The recipes that we are sharing are not only a great source of proteins but they provide your body with a fine quantity of vitamin B, zinc, iron, fiber and other healthy minerals. Here is a list of top 5 Paleo recipes which can help your body muscles to grow healthy:

# Beef and butternut squash Tagine

Fig. 3.0

This delicious dish is first cooked in olive oil with some of other healthy ingredients like cumin, paprika, cinnamon, turmeric, tomato puree, onions, and butternut squash and then it is baked.

The recipe gives you only 8 grams of fat (which is all natural), around 399 calories with 40 grams of carbohydrates and 46 grams of proteins. So, what can be a healthier choice when you can eat baked beef with all the delicious ingredients with such a low fat and rich amount of proteins and natural carbs?

# South Western Steak salad

Fig. 3.1

You love steak but you want to eat paleo so you can stay all healthy? Make this salad a major part of your diet and see the results! You can easily make it with the leftover steak by adding some corn, eggs, onions, pepper, black beans and cook in olive oil. This is a very healthy salad with all the healthy ingredients. Not only this, it tastes heavenly as well.

The salad provides your body with rich amount of natural nutrients with the fat 36 gram, 30 grams of proteins, 28 grams of carbohydrates and only 3 grams of sugar which is equal to having no extra sugar at all. 7 grams of fiber is also there which helps the body to digest food easily and quickly.

# Roast beef melt

Fig. 3.2

People, who want to eat healthy, usually avoid going for foods made out of beef or having beef in them because they think that it will give their body extra fat that they do not even need. Such people should go for roasted beef which is free from extra fat and is a rich source of protein which their body needs for proper growth. Not only this, roast beef also contains iron and zinc which are also very good for body growth.

The dish is very easy to make. You just roast some beef with black peppers, brown bread, and onions in the olive oil and some extra ingredients like mustard and arugula for extra taste. The black pepper does not only gives the dish an amazing taste but it also burns the extra fat so makes the dish all light and tasty. The total fat count present in the dish is only 13 grams with 440 calories, 40 grams proteins, 44 grams of carbohydrates and some fiber.

# Flank steak with chimichurri Sauce

Fig. 3.3

Steak (beef) is a great source of proteins, iron and vitamin B which your body immensely needs for proper and healthy growth. This delicious cuisine makes the beef healthier because you add other very healthy ingredients like garlic, oregano, shallots etc. and cook them together in red wine and some olive oil. You can also add some leafy herbs as well which are also very healthy and your body is always in the need of green vegetables.

The intake of this amazing dish gives you about 295 calories with 22 grams of fat, 24 grams of protein and only 2 grams of fat so people who are always worried about not consuming any fat because of weight issues should definitely go for it!

# Classic Guacamole

Fig. 3.4

We have got something great for all the Guacamole lovers which can be cooked within minutes and is a great source of energy for your body muscles and other organs. All you need to have is some onions, garlic, cilantro, lime, hot sauce, and avocados and the classic guacamole will be ready. The recipe is very easy since all you need to do is crush onions and garlic and turn them into a mince, add some avocados, then add some hot sauce, lime and cilantro. All the ingredients present in this simple recipe are very beneficial for your health and you will not have to compromise on taste as well since the hot sauce and lime makes the dish heavenly.

You get about 167 calories, 17 grams of fat, 2 grams of proteins, 9 grams of carbohydrates, 3 grams of dietary fiber and about 6 grams of net carbs while making this dish a part of your Paleo diet.

# Chapter 4

# Top 5 Ketogenic diet recipes

Many people who want to lose weight stop eating everything because they assume that stopping eating proper meals is that only possible way that they can adapt to remove extra fat from their bodies. But in reality it is not so. If you stop eating proper meals or you skip any meal of the day your body will stop doing functions actively. Skipping the meals should not be seen as the way to lose weight, rather, removing unhealthy foods from your diet and starting to eat only those items which are rich in healthy nutrients should be made the part of daily life. This will result not only in the improved health but you can also reduce your weight by adopting to such kind of diet. Such kind of people can go for ketogenic diet which is one of the best ways to lose weight by not letting your body to compromise on health.

A ketogenic diet is the one which consists of almost no calories, a limited quantity of proteins and a good quantity of natural and healthy fats in it. People usually go for ketogenic diet when they want to lose weight. Their might be some other reasons behind .list of top 5 ketogenic meals:

# Scrambled Eggs (Keto breakfast)

Fig. 4.0

If you want to switch from traditional diet to ketogenic diet then you need to make all the meals of your day ketogenic. It means that you need to start from the morning. As soon as you get up you need to have a proper breakfast (remember that allowing your body to keep starving after you wake up results in unhealthy body and you can clearly never lose weight by skipping the breakfast). So the breakfast needs to be proper but the items that you take should be healthy.

Scrambled eggs is one of the options available if you want to have ketogenic breakfast. You can make them within minutes since all you need to do is make a mince of eggs by mixing them constantly while cooking them in some butter. You can also add a few spoons of milk in them to make them healthier. Black peppers are great to add since they have the ability to burn extra calories and they add delicious taste to your dish too. The healthy benefits of making them a part of your morning meal are that you get about 7 grams of proteins and 8 grams of natural fat as soon as you are about to start your day.

# Creamy Chicken Casserole (Keto meal)

Fig. 4.1

Ketogenic diet has got a wide range of options for your meals as well. You can choose any dishes from the list which will help you to lose weight, stay healthy, and will never even suggest you to compromise on the taste.

Creamy chicken casserole is one of the options. It is a very delicious recipe with a lot of health benefits. You can easily make it by baking chicken with the cream and black peppers and then you can add some leafy vegetables and tomatoes. You get about 18 grams of fat and 35 grams of proteins with 564 calories which can prove to be very beneficial for your health. Eating meals which are made out of all the healthy ingredients can boost your body and you can stay healthy and active throughout your day.

# Eggplant salad (keto sides)

Fig. 4.2

This is one of the recipes that you can eat anytime of the day when you feel hungry and it is not the lunch or breakfast time yet. Because switching to ketogenic diet should not be taken as a diet where you are never allowed to eat anything apart from lunch or dinner. You are allowed to eat whenever you feel like but you should choose to eat only those dishes which can provide you with a good amount of healthy nutrients like fats and proteins, this is a very healthy dish since eggplant is a vegetables full of healthy nutrients. You get only 10 calories, about 8 grams of fat and 2 grams of proteins.

Not only this, the method to make the salad is very easy too. All you need to do is bake eggplants with some bell peppers and then add garlic, black peppers, and green chili to the minced eggplant. You can also add some other green leafy vegetables as well.

# Cheese puffs (keto snacks)

Fig. 4.3

You can live without anything but it is not easy to live without snacks. You always want to eat snacks while working, while watching television or while doing anything. Ketogenic diet suggests you some amazing dishes to east as a snack which are very much beneficial for your health and you will not have to keep yourself starving because you want to lose weight.

You can easily make it within minutes because you only need to make the cubes out of brie cheese, microwave them and serve them by adding black peppers. You intake about 10 grams of fat, 2 grams of proteins and only 10 calories so make this healthy snack a part of your day without wasting any time and stay healthy!

# Crunchy Keto berry Mousse (keto dessert)

Fig. 4.4

No diet is complete without a dessert but people usually think that the diets usually designed for weight lose do not allow you to intake desserts, which is not true because ketogenic diet never makes people to feel like they have to compromise on taste. There is a whole list of healthy and delicious desserts in ketogenic family, crunchy berry mousse is one of them. You can make this mousse easily at home by mixing some barriers and vanilla extract to the whipped cream. The best thing about it is that you consume only 150 calories with 6 grams of protein and 5 gram of fat.

# Chapter 5
# 2-Week Paleo/Keto Meal Plan

Everything seems to be difficult when you are still at the planning stage. But then it's always in your hands to make it as easier as you can by making clear and effective plans for it. Same goes for making plans for your diet. Especially when you are planning about a diet that will help you in losing weight without risking your health, you need to have clear strategies in your mind.

Planning a perfect Paleo/keto diet can also look challenging in the beginning but all you need to have is enough intrinsic and extrinsic motivation and you can easily achieve your goal.

When you aim to lose weight by consuming paleo diet, you need to intake enough animal proteins, vegetables, fruits, nuts, and some healthy fats and avoid taking extra carbs and sugars. You may find it difficult to intake all of these healthy ingredients at the same time. A diet chart or table can be used as a solution to this problem. We can provide a healthy diet chart/table where you will be given healthy meals as your breakfast, lunch, dinner and a snack. By following the chart you can consume all the healthy foods without compromising on taste and health and lose your weight. You are allowed to eat as much as you can by staying in the boundaries of the foods that are suggested in the chart so you will not have to feel like you are on a diet or anything where you will have to stay starving.

# Week 1

| Day | Breakfast | Lunch | Dinner | Snack |
|-----|-----------|-------|--------|-------|
| **MON** | Breakfast Casserole with Sausages (makes 2 days of breakfast; save the leftovers for tomorrow | Portable salad: grab a can of tuna and an avocado with some salad greens, oil, and vinegar, and mix it all up. | Butterflied roasted chicken with wild mushroom soup. (Make stock with the chicken bones) | Piece of fruit |
| **TUE** | Leftover breakfast casserole | Salad with leftover roast chicken, dried cranberries, pecans, apple slices, and vinaigrette. | Ham and Pineapple Skewers with oven-roasted tomatoes (makes 2 servings; save leftovers for snacks) | Carrot sticks with mustard and/or mayo |

| | | | | |
|---|---|---|---|---|
| **WED** | Scrambled Eggs with Smoked Salmon | Leftover roast chicken (cold or hot) inside lettuce wraps with mustard, mayonnaise, or your favorite other condiments | Greek-style meatballs (makes 2 days; save leftovers for lunch tomorrow) with roasted cauliflower | Leftover ham and pineapple skewers (they're great cold!) |
| **THU** | Ham and Butternut Squash Hash (cut recipe in half) | Leftover Greek-style meatballs on top of a big leafy salad with almond slivers and balsamic vinaigrette. | Chicken Pad Sew (makes 2 days; save leftovers for lunch tomorrow) | Banana with almond butter |
| **FRI** | Egg and Vegetable Muffins (makes 2 days; save leftovers for tomorrow) | Leftover chicken Pad Sew | Beef Cubes with Roasted Carrots and Mushrooms (makes 2 days; save leftovers for lunch tomorrow) | Handful of nuts or trail mix |

| SAT | Leftover egg and vegetable muffins | Leftover beef cubes with carrots and mushrooms (add more vegetables on the side if you like) | Garlic Roasted Cod (make ½ recipe) with green beans. | Handful of olives |
| --- | --- | --- | --- | --- |
| **SUN** | Onions, mushrooms, and spinach fried up with bacon or sausages. | Salad with canned salmon, mustard vinaigrette, | Maple Braised Chuck Roast (makes 2 servings; save leftovers for lunch tomorrow) with roasted zucchini | Piece of fruit |

# <u>Week 2</u>

| Day | Breakfast | Lunch | Dinner | Snack |
|---|---|---|---|---|
| **MON** | Apple and Onion Scrambled eggs (make ½ recipe for two people) with some extra fried onions and mushrooms | Leftover maple braised chuck roast | Simple sausage casserole (makes 2 servings; save leftovers for breakfast tomorrow) | Carrot sticks with mustard and/or mayo |
| **TUE** | Leftover sausage casserole | Portable salad: grab a can of tuna and an avocado with some salad greens, oil, and vinegar, and mix it all up. | Beef and Winter Vegetable Soup with oven-roasted eggplant | Frozen berries with a drizzle of coconut milk (and honey if you like) |

| | | | | |
|---|---|---|---|---|
| **WED** | Breakfast stuffed peppers (makes 2 servings; save leftovers for breakfast tomorrow) | Leftover beef and winter vegetable soup | Grilled chicken breasts with zucchini (save half the chicken for lunch tomorrow) | Beef Jerky |
| **THU** | Leftover breakfast stuffed peppers | Leftover grilled chicken breast on top of salad greens with vinaigrette | Spicy Pork Chili (makes 2 days; save leftovers for lunch tomorrow) with pan-fried Brussels sprouts | Piece of fruit |
| **FRI** | Cabbage and onions fried up with bacon | Leftover pork chili with baked sweet potatoes | Pistachio-crusted salmon (makes 2 servings; save leftovers for breakfast tomorrow) with roasted beets and sweet potatoes. | Hard-boiled egg |

| | | | | |
|---|---|---|---|---|
| | | | Roast a double batch of vegetables so you have some for lunch tomorrow. | |
| SAT | Leftover pistachio-crusted salmon served over wilted spinach | Hard-boiled eggs (roughly 3 per person) with leftover roasted vegetables. | Spicy Indian Chicken Stir-Fry with riced cauliflower | Handful of nuts or trail mix |
| SUN | Cherry Tomato and Basil Quiche with extra fried onions | Leftover chicken stir-fry and cauliflower | Ground Beef and Cabbage Skillet (make ½ recipe for 2 people) | Half an avocado sprinkled with sea salt and balsamic vinegar |

After two weeks, you will be able to see clear results in your weight as well as in your health because you would have eaten only healthy foods for whole 15 days and would have avoided all the harmful foods that can stop your body from growing healthy. All the delicious foods that we have suggested in this table like roasted beef, chicken, salmon, green vegetables, onions, eggs, nuts, pork, grilled meats, peppers, olives, sausages, mayo, carrots, tomatoes, custard and fruits contain natural fats, proteins, carbs and other nutrients. Everybody loves eating chicken, pork, beef and salmon and they are healthy too. The difference is that this table suggests healthier versions of them by either grilling or roasting them with fresh vegetables like onions, cauliflower, spinach and olives. Fresh fruits and smoothies are an important part of paleo snacks so you will not have to starve in the evenings or whenever you are bored. The breakfast are also very colorful and tasty where you can eat eggs and vegetables with sausages and bacon. So, enjoy your paleo diet and stay healthy!

# Image References

Fig. 1.0:
http://thepaleodiet.com/wp-content/uploads/2016/01/paleo-table.jpg

Fig. 2.0:
https://www.lovefood.com/recipes/57275/sunflower-chocolate-smoothie-recipe

Fig. 2.1: https://wholefully.com/healthy-pumpkin-pie-smoothie/

Fig. 2.2:
http://www.amafruits.com/images/recipes/rsz_amafruits_smoothie.jpg

Fig. 2.3:
http://www.runningtothekitchen.com/wild-blueberry-beet-smoothie/

Fig. 2.4:
http://www.blendtec.com/blog/green-smoothies-join-the-revolution/

Fig. 3.0: http://www.cookinglight.com/food/top-rated-recipes

Fig. 3.1: https://www.garlicandzest.com/southwestern-steak-salad/

Fig. 3.2:
http://www.kraftrecipes.com/recipes/roast-beef-memphis-melts-126845.aspx

Fig. 3.3: http://www.epicurious.com/recipes/food/views/

Fig. 3.4: http://www.healthyseasonalrecipes.com/classic-guacamole/

Fig. 4.0: http://www.wikihow.com/Scramble-an-Egg

Fig. 4.1: http://www.taste.com.au/recipes/creamy-chicken-casserole/

Fig. 4.2:
http://www.olivetomato.com/greek-eggplant-dip-melitzanosalata/

Fig. 4.3: http://rasamalaysia.com/cheese-puffs-gougeres/

Fig. 4.4:
https://www.mealgarden.com/recipe/crunchy-keto-berry-mousse/

9 781973 829614